Playdays

annual
1994

£4.50
UK only

Honey

Hello Again!

Welcome to the third Playdays Annual -
packed with stories, rhymes and things
to make and do. The playbus has
stopped at the Roundabout Stop and all
your favourite characters are climbing
aboard Rosie to have some fun with
nursery rhymes. Why not turn the page
and join them?

This annual is based on the BBC television programme Playdays produced by Felgate Productions Ltd. for BBC Television.
The BBC logotype and the Playdays logotype are Trademarks of the British Broadcasting Corporation.
"BBC" and "Playdays" are Registered Trademarks of the British Broadcasting Corporation.
All Trademarks are used under non-exclusive licence.

Text © Felgate Productions Ltd. 1993.
Written by Clare Bradley, Kristina Stephenson and Christina Takkides.
Stories: 'Thomas the Rhymer' © Louise Fryer
'Princess Tilly and the Dragon © Eileen Doyle
'King Greenfingers' © Kathleen J. Dean
'The Grumpy Court Jester' © Angela Neville
Edited by Margaret McCarthy.

Designed by Liz Auger.
Illustrated by Kristina Stephenson, Teresa Foster,
Sue Cony, Susie Poole and Ken Morton.
Photographs by Sally Miles.
Hand-lettering by Jeannette Slater.

Published in Great Britain in 1993 by World International Publishing Ltd.,
an Egmont Company, Egmont House,
PO Box III, Great Ducie Street,
Manchester M60 3BL.
Printed in Italy.
ISBN 0 7498 1367 9

CONTENTS

Rosie's Rhyme Time

The Wheels on the Bus

The wheels on the bus go round
    and round
Round and round, round and round,
The wheels on the bus go round
    and round
All day long, long, long.

The people on the bus go yakkety
    yak,
Yakkety yak, yakkety yak,
The people on the bus go yakkety
    yak,
All day long, long, long.

The wipers on the bus go swish,
    swish, swish,
Swish, swish, swish, swish, swish,
    swish.
The wipers on the bus go swish,
    swish, swish,
All day long, long, long.

The driver on the bus goes toot,
    toot, toot,
Toot, toot, toot, toot, toot, toot,
The driver on the bus goes toot,
    toot, toot,
All day long, long, long.

THOMAS the RHYMER

by
Louise Fryer

The Court of Old King Cole was a
wonderful place to be. The King
loved to be entertained and his
palace was full of fiddlers and
drummers, trumpeters, acrobats,
dancers and clowns.

Every evening the King would
settle back in his throne, pipe in one
hand, a big bowl of cereal in the
other, and command the show to
begin. If the King smiled all was well,
but if Old King Cole began to frown
– if a trumpeter played the wrong
note or a juggler dropped a ball –
then the courtiers would rush the
performer away, for at the side of his
throne the King kept an old bucket.

In the bucket was a pile of rotten
fruit. When the King was extremely
displeased he would pelt the
performer with mouldy bananas and
over-ripe tomatoes!

One person who never got pelted
was Thomas the Rhymer. He was a
nursery-rhyme-teller and the King
loved nothing more than to hear a

nursery rhyme before he went to bed.

When he grew tired of clowns and acrobats, Old King Cole would clap his hands and cry, "Enough of all this. Call Thomas the Rhymer," and a tall, rather shy fellow would appear.

"Well Thomas," the King would say, "What rhyme have you written for us today?"

Thomas, who spent the best part of every day in the Royal Orchard inventing new rhymes, would bow politely and mumble "I thought this one might please Your Majesty:
Hickory Dickory Dock,
The mouse ran up the clock,
The clock struck one,
The mouse ran down,
Hickory Dickory Dock."

The King would smile. The courtiers would cheer. "Wonderful, wonderful," the King would say as he yawned happily, and repeating Thomas's rhyme of the day, Old King Cole would retire to bed.

One particularly windy day Thomas was sitting in the Royal Orchard under his favourite apple tree, thinking of rhymes as usual. He was finding it hard to think of something which rhymed with Muffet.

"Er . . . buffet . . tuffet yes, that might do," he said.

Suddenly a large apple blew off the tree and landed with a thud on Thomas's head. Poor Thomas was knocked out!

He didn't come round until late in the evening, when he heard a courtier calling.

"Thomas – oh, there you are. We've been looking for you everywhere. The King's waiting for his nursery rhyme."

Thomas put his hand to his head,

"What King? What's a nursery rhyme?" he groaned.

"Don't be silly," said the courtier, "Come on, we must hurry. The King's very tired, but he won't go to bed without a rhyme."

When Thomas arrived at the palace he was still feeling rather strange and dizzy. Everything looked oddly familiar, but he couldn't quite work out where he was. In front of him was a large throne, with a funny old bucket at the side of it.

"Ah, so you've decided to come at last have you?" grumbled Old King Cole, "It's way past my bedtime. I hope it's a rhyme worth waiting for."

Thomas thought and thought but he couldn't remember a single rhyme.

"Come on, come on," boomed the King.

"Try Jack and Jill," whispered the courtier. "It's one of his favourites." Thomas tried:

"Jack and Jill went up the mountain
To fetch a pail of water
Jack took a tumble and hurt himself
And Jill did as well."

There was a stunned silence. The King frowned.

"Correct me if I'm wrong," he said, "but I don't think that nursery rhyme *rhymes*, does it?"

Thomas shook his head sadly, "I'm sorry Sire, but . . ."

"Try again," whispered the courtier, "Quickly, he's reaching for the fruit."

Thomas racked his brains:

"Hey diddle dee, the cat and the
    violin,
The cow jumped over the moon,
The little dog laughed because he
    thought it was funny
And the dish ran away with a knife
    and fork."

It was no good. Thomas the
Rhymer couldn't remember how to
rhyme. "Pah," growled the King, and
reaching into the bucket he picked
up a large, wasp-bitten apple.

"Duck!" yelled the courtier, but it
was too late and the apple hit
Thomas - *bump* - on the head.

Instantly Thomas felt better. He
remembered the palace, he
remembered the King, he even

remembered what rhymes with
Muffet.

But the King was reaching for
another piece of fruit.

"Wait, wait your majesty. It's all
right. I CAN tell you a nursery
rhyme," and Thomas began a rhyme
he'd been saving for a special
occasion:

*Old King Cole was a merry old soul
and a merry old soul was he,
He called for his pipe
and he called for his bowl
And he called for his fiddlers three."*

The King put an over-ripe tomato
back in the bucket and smiled,

"I like that, yes, it's really rather
good."

Thomas told him the whole rhyme and the fiddlers, the drummers and the trumpeters joined in. The King, quite forgetting his tiredness, started to tap his foot in time to the music and soon the whole court was dancing and singing:

"*Now every trumpeter had a very fine trumpet*
And a very fine trumpet had he,
Pah Pah Pah said the trumpeters,
boom boom boom said the drummers
fiddle diddle dee said the fiddlers
There's none so rare as can compare
with King Cole and his trumpeters three."

And no-one in the court sang as loudly as the King and Thomas the Rhymer.

Why's words

W is for Why.
I like W.

Can you spot 10 things in Why's picture that start with w?

Why's ing words

Which letter starts which word?

k s w r

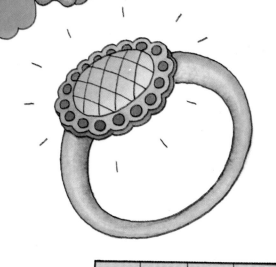

i n g

i n g

i n g

I need this to fly.

i n g

15

Rosie's Rhyme Time

Queen of Hearts

The Queen of Hearts
She made some tarts
All on a summer's day.

The King of Hearts
Called for the tarts
And beat the knave full sore.

The Knave of Hearts
He stole those tarts
And took them clean away.

The Knave of Hearts
Brought back the tarts
And vowed he'd steal no more.

How many tarts can you count?

Dot's Fun WITH SHAPES AND COLOURS

heart   circle   square

What shape is the roof of this house?

Name the colours of the butterflies.

How many are there?

What shapes are in Dot's ice-cream?

Princess Tilly and the Dragon

by Eileen Doyle

Princess Tilly was the nastiest princess in the whole world. She always wanted her own way and was horrible to everyone.

"What would you like for your birthday, dear?" asked the Queen. "A little doll would be very nice."

"Pooh!" said Tilly. "Dolls are stupid."

"Perhaps you'd like a kitten?" said the King.

"Ugh!" cried Tilly, pulling a face. "Kittens are no fun. I want a dragon. A baby dragon!"

"A dragon?" said the King. "Whatever would you do with a dragon?"

"I'd make him into my slave," said Tilly.

"It's out of the question," said the Queen. "Dragons have such bad habits."

So Tilly ran up to the highest tower in the palace, and screamed and screamed and screamed.

The noise was so loud that the King in the next kingdom telephoned to complain.

"All right! All right! We give in," said the King. "You can have your dragon."

"About time, too!" said Tilly.

"It will all end in tears," said the Queen as she ran upstairs for an aspirin.

The baby dragon arrived the next day, fast asleep in his basket. Tilly poked him with a pencil.

"Ouch!" he cried, opening his big yellow eyes. "That's a bit much!"

"Be quiet!" shouted Tilly. "You are my slave."

"No-one said anything about that," said the dragon, looking puzzled.

23

"By the way, my name is Norman and I need some hot milk."

"I'm a princess," said Tilly. "Not a maid."

"Please yourself," said Norman. "But I won't grow big and fierce without my hot milk."

When the milk was finished, Norman took a piece of paper from under his pillow. "Now, let's see," he said. "What's next?"

Tilly frowned. "Next?" she asked. "What do you mean?"

"Well," said Norman. "This is a list of all the things a baby dragon needs." He held it out. It was very, very long.

Tilly was beginning to wish she'd chosen a kitten.

"I'll have my dummy now," said Norman, settling down under his blankets. "And don't forget the hot water bottle!"

"But you're supposed to be MY slave," cried Tilly.

"Later! Later!" murmured Norman, closing his eyes.

Tilly rushed out to the chemists and bought the biggest dummy she could find. Then she dashed back to the palace kitchen and filled her favourite rabbit hot water bottle. By the time she got back to Norman, he was looking at his watch and frowning.

"You took your time," he said. "Where's my dummy?"

He took one lick and squealed. "Ugh! Yucky yoo! You've forgotten to dip it in sugar."

But the hot water bottle was a success. "Yippee! A bunny!" cried Norman and he went to sleep with his arms wrapped round the rabbit's neck.

Baby dragons are lovable little creatures and remain babies for 84 years. Then they begin to crawl.

The King and Queen were having a nice cup of tea when Tilly burst in. "He's got to go!" she said. "I'll be old and grey before he's even crawling."

Just then the telephone rang. "Hello," said Tilly crossly.

"This is Norman's auntie," said a deep voice. "Will you tell the King we would like him back. We miss him very much! And, by the way, we hope he did the trick."

Tilly replaced the receiver with a bang. "What trick?" she asked.

The King was very red in the face. "We wanted to teach you a lesson," he said.

"We thought you'd be nicer if you were busy," said the Queen. Tilly rubbed her chin. "I *am* nicer," she said. "I haven't had time to be anything else!"

The King and Queen smiled. It was time for Norman to go home.

"Well, I'm glad he's pleased with something," said Tilly. "But I suppose I'll have to freeze tonight!"

Then she suddenly remembered that she hadn't eaten since breakfast time.

As she was creeping out to grab a sandwich, Norman called out. "Don't forget my rattle. A baby dragon needs a rattle. And make sure it's red. Red is my favourite colour."

On the way back from the baby shop, Tilly called in at the library. She found an enormous book about dragons and turned to B for baby. She began to read it aloud.

"*Baby Dragons are lovable little creatures and remain babies for 84 years. Then they begin to crawl.*"

"Oh no," shouted Tilly. "What have I done? He's ruined my life."

Make a DRAGON!

BITSY BOB, CAN YOU HELP US?

We need:

an egg box

paper and card

felt tips
scissors
sticky tape

glue
and some
other boxes

1 Draw 2 circles on the card.

2 Now cut them out.

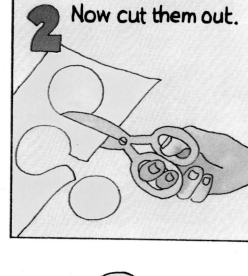

3 Colour some eyes.

4 Stick the eyes on to the egg box.

26

5 Sticky tape the boxes together.

6 Cut out a point for the tail.

7 Fold 2 paper fans for wings.

MORRIS AND MILLY! WHAT A LOVELY DRAGON!

8 Fix the tail and the wings on with sticky tape.

27

Rosie's Rhyme Time

Sing a Song of Sixpence

Sing a song of sixpence
A pocket full of rye.
Four and twenty blackbirds
Baked in a pie.
When the pie was opened –
The birds began to sing.
Wasn't that a dainty dish
To set before the King.

The King was in his counting house
Counting out his money.
The Queen was in the parlour
Eating bread and honey.
The maid was in the garden
Hanging out the clothes -
When down came a blackbird
And pecked off her nose.

Then along came Jenny Wren
Who stuck her nose back on again.

BIRDWATCHING

Lizzie and Chester are birdwatching. Can you see 10 blackbirds hiding in the playground?

MAKE A CROWN

You need:

thin card

sweet papers,
buttons,
milk bottle tops,
tissue paper,
cotton wool

sticky tape

glue

scissors

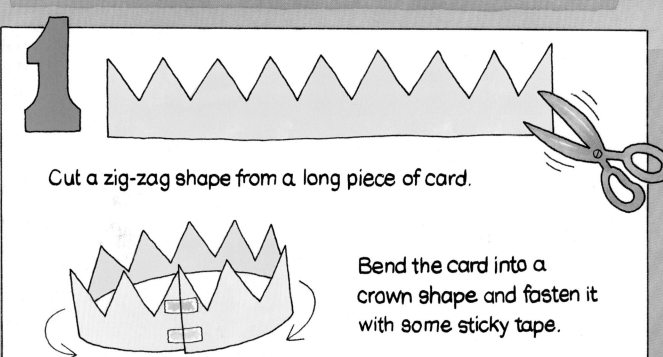

1

Cut a zig-zag shape from a long piece of card.

Bend the card into a
crown shape and fasten it
with some sticky tape.

2

Cut two long thin strips from card.

Bend them into arch shapes and stick them onto the crown.

3

Cut a circle from tissue paper and glue it to the inside of the crown.

4

Now you can decorate your crown with milk bottle tops, buttons, coloured shapes and some cotton wool fur.

KING GREENFINGERS
by Kathleen J Dean
STRAWBERRIES FOR THE MAYOR

One warm sunny morning King Greenfingers leapt out of bed, threw open the windows and declared, "What a simply beautiful day for picking strawberries."

His wife, Queen Climbing Rose, yawned and tripped to the window to join him. "No Greenfingers," she said gently, "It's a simply beautiful day to open a garden fête and make a speech because that is what kings have to do on beautiful sunny days."

"Oh," said the King, his smile disappearing, "is it, er, do they?"

"Now surely you haven't forgotten that the Mayor asked weeks ago if we would open his garden fête so you could make one of your lovely speeches?

"All sorts of important guests will be there and we'll have tea and cucumber sandwiches and . . ."

Greenfingers groaned. "But my love, the strawberries must be picked before they get too ripe. You know how you like to make jams and flans and strawberry cakes at this time of year."

"That's true," agreed the Queen as she went to run the Royal bath.

When the King was bathed and ready the Queen let him go to the strawberry patch to pick a few strawberries for the Mayor. "Don't get dirty and be back by one o'clock," said the Queen, "or the Royal coach will go without you."

The smile returned to King Greenfinger's face and he was soon in the strawberry patch with a large basket. As he picked the strawberries he sang a song:

"One in the basket, one in the tummy,
One in the basket, these are so scrummy.
Strawberries for breakfast, dinner and tea,
A few for you and a few for me."

King Greenfingers should not have eaten so many strawberries. He was soon asleep in the strawberry patch dreaming of strawberry jam, flans and cream cakes with strawberries.

He was awakened by the sound of a tractor. Farmer Blenkinsop was working in the field next to the Palace. He stopped the tractor and peered over the wall.

"Fine strawberries you have there your majesty," said Farmer Blenkinsop, his mouth watering.

"I'll pick you some if you like," offered the King. "Haymaking must be hungry work."

"It certainly is," said Farmer Blenkinsop. "It can only be half an hour since dinner but I'm already hungry." King Greenfingers suddenly stopped picking. "Farmer Blenkinsop has had his dinner, it must be past one o'clock" he thought. "And if it's past one o'clock, the Royal coach must have gone to the Mayor's fête without me, for Royal coachmen wait for no one, not even the King."

Farmer Blenkinsop saw that the King was looking very glum. The King explained his problem. "I can take you there, if you would like me to," said the kind farmer.

King Greenfingers was very grateful and settled himself comfortably in the cart with his basket.

FETE HERE TODAY!

When they
got to the Mayor's
mansions, Farmer Blenkinsop
pulled up with a jerk and
King Greenfingers slid to the
ground with a bump, his
crown following after.
He picked himself up
and entered the Mayor's
garden dusting off the bits
of straw as he went.

What a crowd of angry faces met his eyes, for it was long past the fête's opening time. His daughter, the Princess Potted Palm, dashed over to her father.

"Daddy, make a speech. That will make them feel happier."

Speech! Oh goodness, he'd forgotten that too!

King Greenfingers straightened his crown, took a deep breath and faced them all.

"Er, it gives me great pleasure," he started, "it gives me great pleasure, er to pick strawberries - and I'd like you all to have some."

"Hurray," shouted the crowd, "Magnificent speech. Hurray for King Greenfingers."

Then they all dashed into a big marquee and ate strawberries until they felt like bursting. All except King Greenfingers. He had eaten quite enough strawberries. Instead the King had a plate of cucumber sandwiches all to himself!

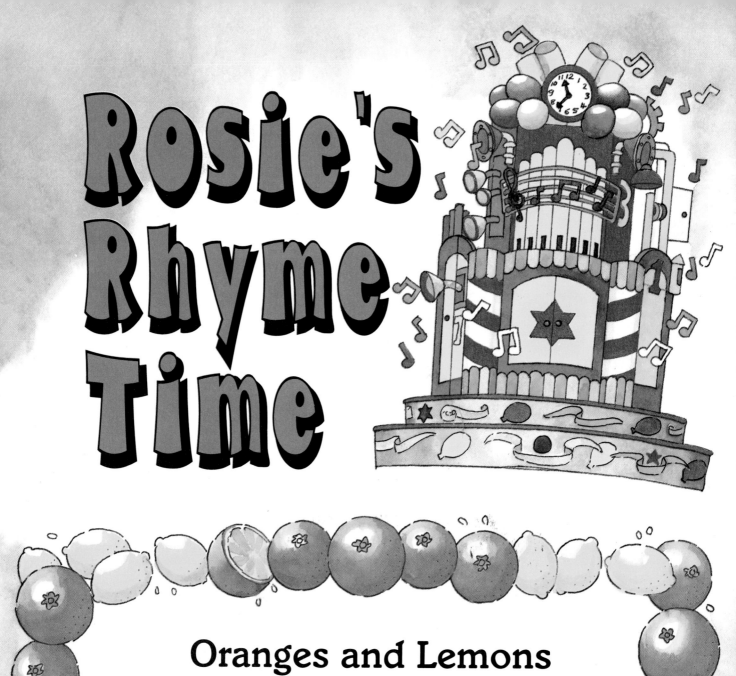

Rosie's Rhyme Time

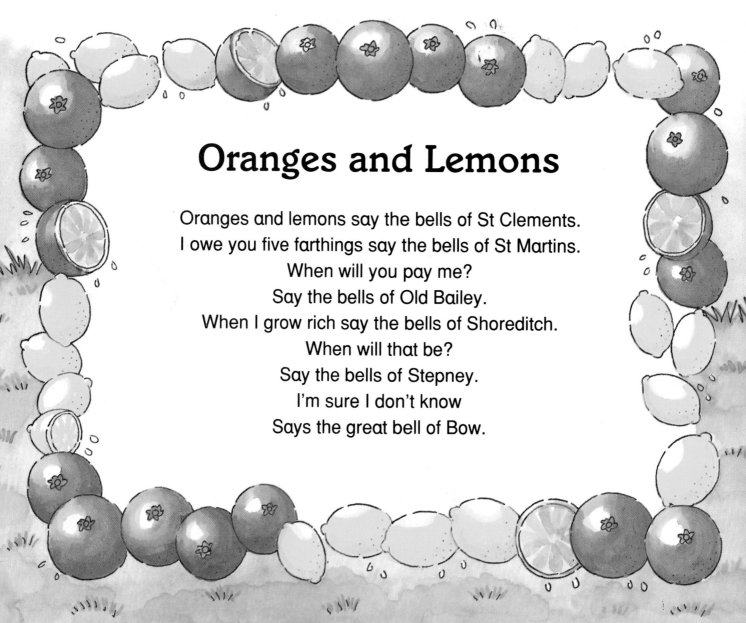

Oranges and Lemons

Oranges and lemons say the bells of St Clements.
I owe you five farthings say the bells of St Martins.
When will you pay me?
Say the bells of Old Bailey.
When I grow rich say the bells of Shoreditch.
When will that be?
Say the bells of Stepney.
I'm sure I don't know
Says the great bell of Bow.

How many bells
can you count?

Can you find 2 the same?

There are 5 pairs.

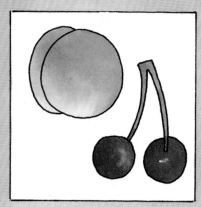

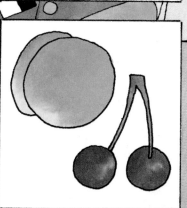

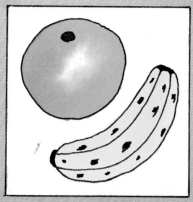

JOKE

What did one banana say to the other banana?
Nothing – bananas can't talk!

The Grumpy Court Jester

by Angela Neville

When the Queen walked into the royal throne room one morning, she found the King, the Princes and the Princesses all looking decidedly distressed.

"Whatever is the matter?" she asked.

"It's the court jester," whispered the King, looking rather scared. "He seems to have gone a bit, you know, funny."

"Well of course he's funny," said the Queen. "It's his job. He's just won the competition for Funniest Court Jester in the world."

"Well, now the only competition he'll win is for the most thoroughly grumpy court jester!" said the King. "He has forgotten all his songs, all his little dances, all his jokes; everything that made him funny."

Later, the court jester was sitting on the royal throne looking as grumpy as anyone could. "What do you want?" he asked rudely.

"Well, I wondered," said the King, "if I could have my throne back, please and —"

"No!" said the jester. The King was speechless.

"I know what we'll do!" said the Queen, and she whispered her plan to the others.

They all put on red noses and funny hats.

The Queen did a splendid cartwheel.

The Princes told their best jokes.

The Princesses did a silly dance.

Finally, the King walked on his hands.

But, the jester didn't laugh or smile even once. He just sat there, scowling more fiercely than before. "Rubbish!" he said rudely.

After that, all sorts of people came to try to cure the court jester. Doctors came to examine him. Other jesters tried to cheer him up. But, the jester was so grumpy that some of the people went home in tears. Some of the jesters were so upset that they could never work as jesters again and had to find other jobs.

Finally, no one else would come. The jester was just too grumpy.

"Oh dear!" said the Queen, "and we've got the King, the Queen and the Princess of Smugdonia coming to stay next week. Just think what will happen if the jester is rude to them!"

The King gulped.

Just then there was a ring on the door bell, and in came a very small woman carrying a very large bag. "How do you do," she said. "I'm a She-Wiz and I've come to cure your court jester."

"Hooray!" cried the royals.

"Can you give me all the details please?" she said, taking out a notebook and pencil.

So they told her all about their thoroughly grumpy court jester.

"Mmm," she said, pacing up and down. "Now, what cure can we try? What about – no! Too messy! How about – no! Never get rid of the smell! I know!" she suddenly cried.

"What?" asked the royals.

"Just wait and see," chuckled the She-Wiz.

She took a strange parcel out of her bag. Then she unwrapped something round and flat and held it up to the court jester.

The jester scowled at it fiercely – but then, something began to happen. He gave a little grin. The grin turned into a beaming smile.

He began to chuckle, the chuckle turned into a laugh. Soon the jester was roaring with laughter. He laughed so hard that he rolled off the throne and on to the floor.

"It's . . . it's the funniest thing I've ever seen!" he spluttered.

"What is it?" said the King.

"What can it be?" said the Queen.

The She-Wiz showed them.

"Why, it's a mirror!" cried the Princes and Princesses.

"You said he used to be the funniest court jester in the world," said the She-Wiz. "So only the funniest court jester could cheer him up again."

Everyone laughed. The court jester laughed the loudest of all, and never needed to look in the mirror again.

But they kept it anyway – just in case!

Chester's sad day

[Chester] was sad, all his friends on the [van] had forgotten his birthday. [Chester] had waited in all morning and no [cards] had come or [presents]. Even the [telephone] had not rung. [Chester] felt very sad, he did not want to eat his [cake] alone. [Chester] decided to go out for a walk. He opened the [door] and

SURPRISE! HAPPY BIRTHDAY CHESTER!

[Chester's] sad face turned into a happy face.

How does WOBBLE FEEL?

Wobble is... sad.

Wobble is... angry.

Wobble is... surprised.

Wobble is... happy.

Wobble is...puzzled.

Wobble is...worried.

Wobble is...sleepy.

Draw a picture to show how <u>you</u> feel today.

Rosie's Rhyme Time

1 · 2 · 3 · 4 · 5

One, two, three, four, five
Once I caught a fish alive.
Six, seven, eight, nine, ten
Then I let it go again.
Why did I let it go?
Because it bit my finger so.
Which finger did it bite?
This little finger on the right.

ouch!

How many fish can you count?

MAKE A FISH

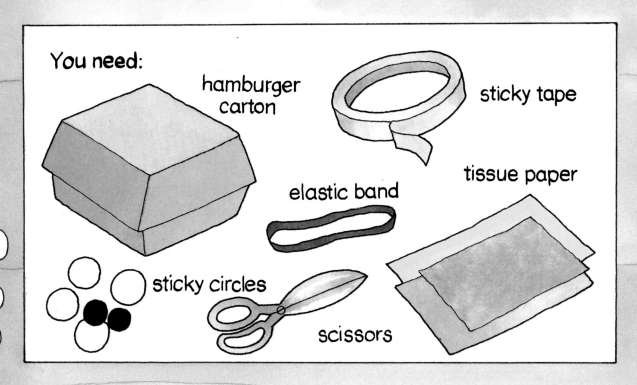

You need:

hamburger carton

sticky tape

tissue paper

elastic band

sticky circles

scissors

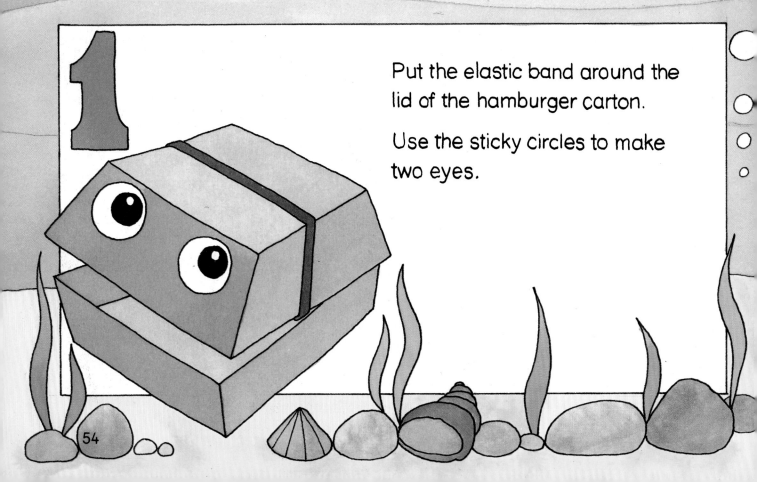

1

Put the elastic band around the lid of the hamburger carton.

Use the sticky circles to make two eyes.

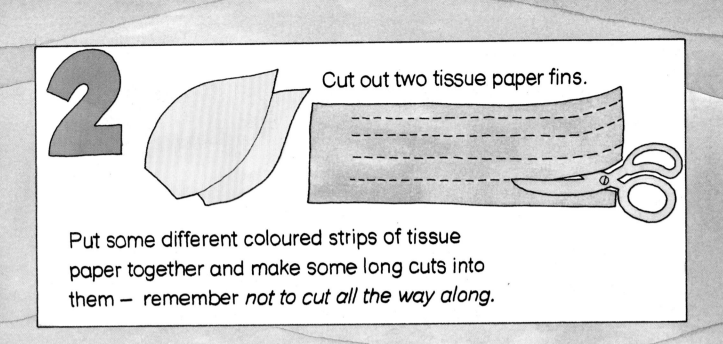

2

Cut out two tissue paper fins.

Put some different coloured strips of tissue paper together and make some long cuts into them — remember *not to cut all the way along.*

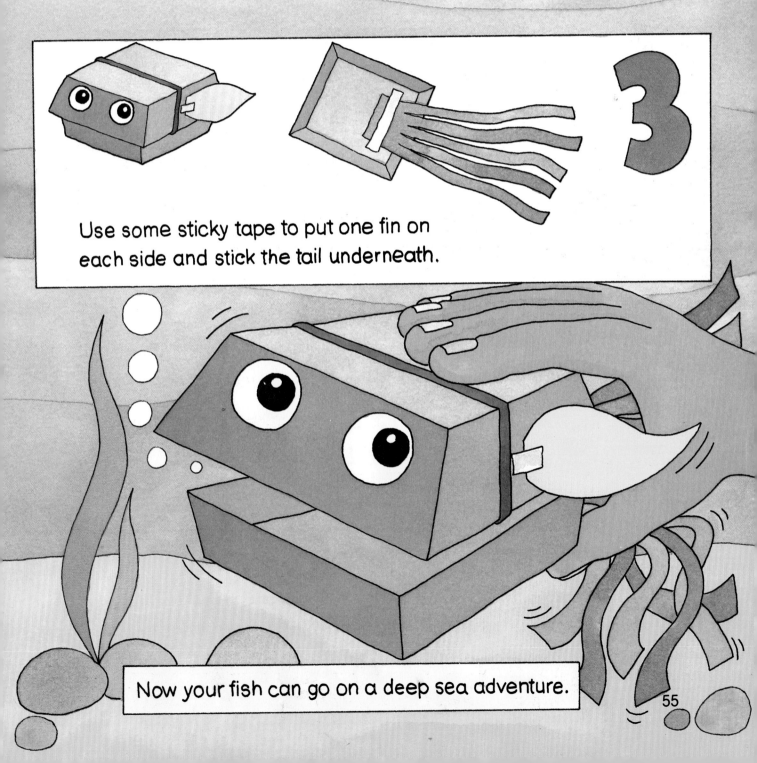

3

Use some sticky tape to put one fin on each side and stick the tail underneath.

Now your fish can go on a deep sea adventure.

Sitting by the River.

Mr Jolly, Wobble, Humphrey and Chester are fishing.
Can you follow their lines to see what they have caught?

How many fish can you see?

It's Panto Time!

Sleeping Beauty

This is the story of a Princess who pricks her finger on a spinning wheel and falls asleep for one hundred years. Only a prince can wake her with a kiss . . .

Can you find:

1 2 3

Once Upon a Time...

You are invited to a Ball (that's a grand party where everyone dresses very smart and there is lots of dancing). You will need a counter or button for each player and a dice. Throw the dice to see how many squares to move. The first player to reach the palace is the winner!

4 Stop to buy and plant 3 magic beans and miss a go!

3

5

13 You take flight with mother goose and move forward 2 spaces.

12

2

6

11

1

7 You find Cinderella's slipper and move forward 2 spaces.

10 Rub Aladdin's magic lamp and move forward 2 spaces.

Start

8

9

FINISH

30 You have arrived at the Royal Ball and all your friends are waiting for you.

29

28 Climb Jack's beanstalk and miss a go.

27

26

25 You find a golden egg and move forward 2 spaces.

24

23

22 You stop to play with Princess Beauty's spinning wheel and miss a go.

21

20

15

16 You stop to eat at the gingerbread house and miss a go.

17

18

19 You see a wolf — wait behind the tree until he has gone and miss a go.